GREAT MINDS® WIT & WISDOM

Grade 2 Module 3:
Civil Rights Heroes

Student Edition

COPYRIGHT STATEMENT

Table of Contents

Handout 20A: Shades of Meaning

Handout 21A: SCPAE Chart

Handout 21B: Sentence Variety

Handout 22A: Sentence Variety

Handout 23A: Narrative Writing Checklist

Handout 24A: Fluency Homework

Handout 24B: Compound Words

Handout 27A: Response Cards

Handout 28A: Narrative Writing Checklist

Handout 28B: Compound Words

Handout 29A: Prefixes *bi-* and *tri-*

Handout 31A: End-of-Module Task Pre-Writing

Handout 33A: Narrative Writing Checklist

Handout 34A: Socratic Seminar Self-Reflection

Volume of Reading Reflection Questions

Wit & Wisdom Parent Tip Sheet

Name:

Handout 2A: Question Cube

Directions: Cut out the shape below and fold on the dotted lines. Tape along the edges to form a cube. Roll the cube and form a question using the resulting word.

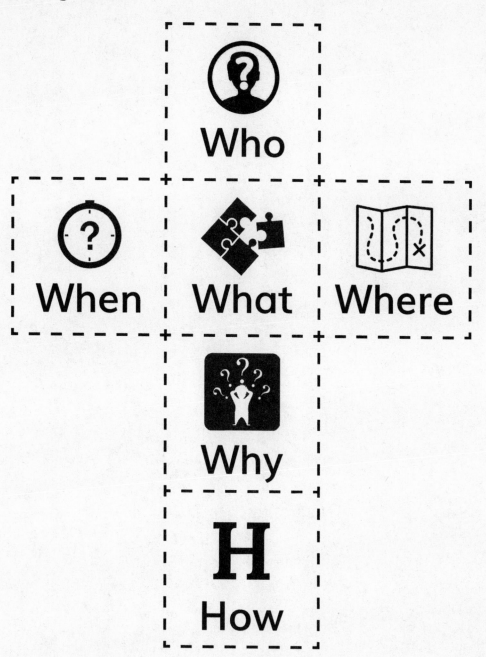

Name:

Handout 2B: Fluency Homework

Directions: Choose one of the text options to read for homework. Have an adult or peer initial the unshaded boxes each day that you read the passage.

Option A

The man's name is Martin Luther King Jr.

He is a preacher and the son of a preacher.

He has grown up in Georgia. He knows all about what it is like to be a black person in the South.

Dr. King is a man of peace. But he is also a fighter. He doesn't use his fists or weapons. He uses words. In the South, Dr. King has led many other protests. One was a march in Georgia. Another was a protest against a bus company in Alabama.

89 words

Ruffin, Frances E. *Martin Luther King, Jr. and the March on Washington.* Penguin Young Readers, 2001.

Student Performance Checklist:	Day 1		Day 2		Day 3		Day 4	
	You	Listener*	You	Listener*	You	Listener*	You	Listener*
Read the passage three to five times.								
Read with appropriate phrasing and pausing.								
Read with appropriate expression.								
Read at a good pace, not too fast and not too slow.								
Read to be heard and understood.								

*Adult or peer

Name:

Option B

It is because one hundred years ago, President Lincoln helped to free the people who were slaves.

It was during the Civil War.

President Lincoln knew that slavery had to end.

Now it is 1963.

There has been no slavery for a long time.
But are black people and white people treated equally?
No.

And that is why people are in Washington today.

They have come to protest.

They will speak out against something they think is wrong.

78 words

Ruffin, Frances E. *Martin Luther King, Jr. and the March on Washington.* Penguin Young Readers, 2001.

Student Performance Checklist:	Day 1		Day 2		Day 3		Day 4	
	You	Listener*	You	Listener*	You	Listener*	You	Listener*
Read the passage three to five times.								
Read with appropriate phrasing and pausing.								
Read with appropriate expression.								
Read at a good pace, not too fast and not too slow.								
Read to be heard and understood.								

*Adult or peer

Name:

Handout 4A: Connecting Historical Events

Instructions: Cut out the boxes below and place the historical events in order.

There was slavery in the country.

In 1963, black people were still not treated fairly.

President Lincoln helped end slavery.

Name:

Handout 4B: Evidence Organizer

Directions: Complete the Evidence Organizer with evidence from the book and the video to prepare for the Focusing Question Task.

Focusing Question Task: What were the injustices people faced before the Civil Rights Act of 1964?		
Introduction:		
Topic Statement:		
	Sources	
	Book	Video
Evidence 1		
Evidence 2		
Evidence 3		
Conclusion:		

Name: _____

Handout 4C: Word Relationships

Directions:
1. Cut apart the words below the chart.
2. Sort the words under either integration or segregation.

Integration	Segregation

separate	apart	unfair	Jim Crow	justice
join	injustice	Civil Rights	together	fair

Name:

Handout 5A: Lyrics to "Ain't Gonna Let Nobody Turn Me Around"

Directions: Use these lyrics to follow along with the song.

Ain't Gonna Let Nobody Turn Me Around

Ain't gonna let nobody turn me 'round
Turn me 'round, turn me 'round
Ain't gonna let nobody turn me 'round
I'm gonna keep on walkin' Keep on talkin'
Marchin' to that freedom land

Ain't gonna let segregation turn me 'round
Turn me 'round, turn me 'round
Ain't gonna let segregation turn me 'round
I'm gonna keep on walkin' Keep on talkin'
Marchin' to that freedom land

Ain't gonna let Jim Crow turn me 'round
Turn me 'round, turn me 'round
Ain't gonna let Jim Crow turn me 'round
I'm gonna keep on walkin' Keep on talkin'
Marchin' to that freedom land

Name:

Ain't gonna let Bull Conner turn me 'round
Turn me 'round, turn me 'round
Ain't gonna let Bull Conner turn me 'round
I'm gonna keep on walkin' Keep on talkin'
Marchin' to that freedom land

Ain't gonna let nobody turn me 'round
Turn me 'round, turn me 'round
Ain't gonna let nobody turn me 'round
I'm gonna keep on walkin' Keep on talkin'
Marchin' to that freedom land

Performed by Stephen Griffith
Original author unknown

Name:

Handout 5B: Adverbs

Directions:

1) Complete the sentence frame, **The adverb** _____
   describes how_____ .

2) Circle the word being described.

3) Draw an arrow from the adverb to the word being described.

4) Reflect on why writers use adverbs.

Example:

But are black people and white people (treated) equally?
The adverb equally describes how people were treated.

Your turn:

1. The people marched slowly.

   The adverb_____describes how_____.

2. The people clapped loudly for Dr. King.

   The adverb_____describes how_____.

Name:

3. Black and white people had to sit separately.

   The adverb _____ describes how _____.

4. Martin Luther King Jr. treated people fairly.

   The adverb _____ describes how _____.

Why do writers use adverbs?

_____

_____

_____

Name:

Handout 6A: Informative Writing Checklist

Directions: After completing your informative paragraph, circle ☺ Yes or ☺ Not Yet to answer each prompt. Be sure to include a writing goal.

Reading Comprehension	Self		Peer		Teacher	
I understand the injustices that people faced before the Civil Rights Act of 1964.	Yes	Not Yet	Yes	Not Yet	Yes	Not Yet
Structure	**Self**		**Peer**		**Teacher**	
I start the paragraph with an introduction.	Yes	Not Yet	Yes	Not Yet	Yes	Not Yet
I include a topic statement.	Yes	Not Yet	Yes	Not Yet	Yes	Not Yet
I include at least two points with evidence.	Yes	Not Yet	Yes	Not Yet	Yes	Not Yet

Name:

I end the paragraph with a conclusion.	🙂 😐 Yes Not Yet	🙂 😐 Yes Not Yet	🙂 😐 Yes Not Yet
Development	**Self**	**Peer**	**Teacher**
I choose important points that support the topic statement.	🙂 😐 Yes Not Yet	🙂 😐 Yes Not Yet	🙂 😐 Yes Not Yet
I clearly explain my points using details.	🙂 😐 Yes Not Yet	🙂 😐 Yes Not Yet	🙂 😐 Yes Not Yet
Style	**Self**	**Peer**	**Teacher**
I use topic-specific words.	🙂 😐 Yes Not Yet	🙂 😐 Yes Not Yet	🙂 😐 Yes Not Yet
I use two sources to collect my evidence for my paragraph.	🙂 😐 Yes Not Yet	🙂 😐 Yes Not Yet	🙂 😐 Yes Not Yet
Total # of 🙂 :			

Name:

My writing goal is

_____

_____

_____

Teacher Feedback

Name:

Handout 7A: Fluency Homework

Directions: Read the text for homework. Have an adult or peer initial the unshaded boxes each day that you read the passage.

I have a dream that my four little children will one day live in a nation where they will not be judged by the color of their skin but by the content of their character.

I have a dream today.

I have a dream that one day... little black boys and black girls will be able to join hands with little white boys and white girls as sisters and brothers. I have a dream today.

75 words

King, Martin Luther, Jr. *I Have a Dream*. 1963.
Illustrated by Kadir Nelson, Random House Children's Books, 2012.

Student Performance Checklist:	Day 1		Day 2		Day 3		Day 4	
	You	Listener*	You	Listener*	You	Listener:	You	Listener*
Read the passage three to five times.								
Read with appropriate phrasing and pausing.								
Read with appropriate expression.								
Read at a good pace, not too fast and not too slow.								
Read to be heard and understood.								

*Adult or peer

Name:

Handout 7B: Root Word *Equal*

Directions: Complete Part 1 and Part 2 below.

Part 1:

   1 Underline the root word in each word:

        equality   *equally*

   2. What do the words *equality* and *equally* have in common?

   _____

   _____

Fit the following words in the sentences below: *equality, equally, equal.*

   3. Black and white people were not being treated _____ .

   4. Dr. King wanted _____ for all people, no matter the color of their skin.

   5. Things were not _____ for black and white people.

Part 2:

6. Write a sentence about Dr. King's hope for a better world, using the word *equality*, *equally*, or *equal*.

_____

_____

_____

Name:

Handout 8A: Identifying Adjectives

Directions:

1. Underline the descriptive word and circle the word being described.

2. Draw an arrow showing the connection.

3. Fill in the sentence frame.

4. Come up with another adjective that could fit in the sentence.

Example:

Let freedom ring from the (mighty) mountains of New York.

The adjective <u>mighty</u> describes the noun <u>mountains</u>.

1. *Martin Luther King gave a powerful speech.*

   The adjective_____describes the noun_____.

   Another adjective: _____

2. *A large crowd gathered to listen to Dr. King's speech.*

   The adjective_____describes the noun_____.

   Another adjective: _____

3. *It is a hot day in Washington D.C.*

   The adjective_____describes the noun_____.

   Another adjective: _____

4. *The crowd grows quiet.*

   The adjective_____describes the noun_____.

   Another adjective: _____

Name:

Handout 9A: Response Cards for Dream Circles

Directions: Cut out the Response Cards below and sort them into two groups: one group of all the details that relate to Martin Luther King Jr.'s dream for *children*, and another group of all the details that relate to his dream for the *states/nation*.

The nation will "rise up and live out the true meaning of its creed."	In Georgia, the sons of former slaves and the sons of former slave owners will be able to sit down together.
Mississippi will become "an oasis of freedom and justice."	My four children will not be judged by the color of their skin.
Little black boys and girls will join hands with little white boys and girls.	Freedom will ring from the Rockies in Colorado.
All God's children will sing *My Country 'Tis of Thee* with new meaning.	Freedom will ring from the hilltops of New Hampshire.

Name:

Freedom will ring from the mountains of New York.	Freedom will ring from the slopes of California.
Freedom will ring from Mississippi.	Freedom will ring "from every state."
"All God's children... will be able to join hands and sing..."	We will transform our nation into a "beautiful symphony of brotherhood."

Name: _____

Handout 9B: Adverbs

Directions:

1. Circle the verb in the sentence.

2. Ask a "how" question about the verb. For example, "How did Dr. King speak?"

3. Write an adverb on the blank to expand and improve the sentence.

4. Draw an arrow from the adverb to the verb.

1. The children play _____ with each other.

2. The children play _____ with each other.

3. The children _____ play with each other.

4. The marchers listened _____ to Dr. King.

5. The marchers watch Dr. King _____ .

6. Dr. King treated people _____ .

7. The marchers walk _____ .

8. The marchers walk _____ .

Name:

Handout 10A: Comparing Adjectives and Adverbs

Directions:

1. Underline the descriptive word.

2. Circle the word being described.

3. Ask yourself, "is the word I circled a noun or a verb?"

4. Decide if the underlined word is an adverb or an adjective.

	Adjective	Adverb
Dr. King spoke proudly to the crowd.		
Dr. King was a kind man.		
Ruby speaks kindly to others.		
The people sang sweetly.		
My country 'tis of thee, sweet land of liberty.		
The red hills of Georgia.		

1. **How are adjectives and adverbs different?**

   Adjectives describe_____, but adverbs describe_____.

2. **When would a writer choose an adjective and when would a writer choose an adverb?**

   _____

   _____

   _____

Name:

Handout 11A: Introduction/ Conclusion Organizer

Directions: Use the following pages from Martin Luther King, Jr. and the March on Washington to help you draft your introduction and conclusion statements.

Focusing Question Task: What was Martin Luther King's dream?		
Introduction Statement	*Who was Martin Luther King Jr.?* Reread pages 32–34.	
Conclusion Statement	*What impact did Martin Luther King Jr.'s speech have?* Reread pages 41–47.	

Name:

Handout 11B: Prefix *re–*

Directions:

1. Cut out the prefixes and base words.

2. Create new words.

3. Write the definitions of the new words you created.

un	re	heat
un	re	appear
un	re	use
dis	re	pack
re	re	fill
re	re	start
re	un	write
un	tie	name

Name:

Handout 12A: Informative Writing Checklist

Directions: After completing your informative paragraph, circle ☺ Yes or 😐 Not Yet to answer each prompt. Be sure to include a writing goal.

Reading Comprehension	Self	Peer	Teacher
I understand Martin Luther King's dream for the world.	☺ 😐 Yes Not Yet	☺ 😐 Yes Not Yet	☺ 😐 Yes Not Yet
Structure	**Self**	**Peer**	**Teacher**
I start the paragraph with an introduction.	☺ 😐 Yes Not Yet	☺ 😐 Yes Not Yet	☺ 😐 Yes Not Yet
I include a topic statement.	☺ 😐 Yes Not Yet	☺ 😐 Yes Not Yet	☺ 😐 Yes Not Yet
I include at least two points with evidence.	☺ 😐 Yes Not Yet	☺ 😐 Yes Not Yet	☺ 😐 Yes Not Yet

Name:

I end the paragraph with a conclusion.	☺ ☺ Yes Not Yet	☺ ☺ Yes Not Yet	☺ ☺ Yes Not Yet
Development	Self	Peer	Teacher
I choose important points that support the topic statement.	☺ ☺ Yes Not Yet	☺ ☺ Yes Not Yet	☺ ☺ Yes Not Yet
I clearly explain my points using details.	☺ ☺ Yes Not Yet	☺ ☺ Yes Not Yet	☺ ☺ Yes Not Yet
Style	Self	Peer	Teacher
I use topic-specific words.	☺ ☺ Yes Not Yet	☺ ☺ Yes Not Yet	☺ ☺ Yes Not Yet
I use two sources to collect my evidence for my paragraph.	☺ ☺ Yes Not Yet	☺ ☺ Yes Not Yet	☺ ☺ Yes Not Yet
Total # of ☺:			

Name:

My writing goal is

_____

_____

_____

Teacher Feedback

Name:

Handout 12B: Frayer Model

Directions: Complete the Frayer Model for *freedom*.

Definition:	Facts/Characteristics:
The ability to act and speak as one wants.	

Word:

freedom

Examples:	Non-Examples:

Name:

Handout 13A: Socratic Seminar Self-Reflection

Directions: Use one of the letters below to describe how often you performed each action during the Socratic Seminar.

A = I always did that.
S = I sometimes did that.
N = I'll do that next time.

Expectation	Evaluation (A, S, N)
I spoke on topic.	
I listened for the main topic.	
I looked at the speaker.	
I spoke only when no one else was speaking.	
I used kind words.	
I varied inflection when speaking.	

Name: _____

Handout 13B: Compound Words

Directions:

1) Cut the compound word into two smaller words.

2) Sketch a symbol or picture on the back of each word showing its meaning.

3) Put the two images together and use the words' meanings to think of the meaning of the compound word.

4) Tape the compound word into your Vocabulary Journals and write or draw its definition.

hilltop

mountainside

Name: _____

afternoon

desktop

classmate

Student Performance Checklist:	Day 1		Day 2		Day 3		Day 4	
	You	Listener*	You	Listener*	You	Listener*	You	Listener*
Read the passage three to five times.								
Read with appropriate phrasing and pausing.								
Read with appropriate expression.								
Read at a good pace, not too fast and not too slow.								
Read to be heard and understood.								

*Adult or peer

Name: _____

Handout 14B: Experiment with Adjectives and Adverbs

Directions:

1) Pull a card from the pile and decides whether the word on the card is a noun or a verb.

2) Decide whether you will describe the word with an adjective or an adverb.

3) Create a sentence using the word card and the describing word. Write down the sentence.

4) Group members share their sentences with each other.

5) Repeat.

My sentences:

Word Card:_____   NOUN or VERB

Descriptive Word: _____   ADJECTIVE or ADVERB

Sentence: _____

Word Card: _____   NOUN or VERB

Descriptive Word: _____   ADJECTIVE or ADVERB

Sentence: _____

Name: _____

Word Card: _____ NOUN or VERB

Descriptive Word: _____ ADJECTIVE or ADVERB

Sentence: _____

Word Card: _____ NOUN or VERB

Descriptive Word: _____ ADJECTIVE or ADVERB

Sentence: _____

Word Card:_____ NOUN or VERB

Descriptive Word: _____ ADJECTIVE or ADVERB

Sentence: _____

Word Card:_____ NOUN or VERB

Descriptive Word: _____ ADJECTIVE or ADVERB

Sentence: _____

Name:
_____

Word Card: _____ NOUN or VERB

Descriptive Word: _____ ADJECTIVE or ADVERB

Sentence: _____

Explain why you chose an adjective or adverb in one of your sentences:

_____

_____

_____

_____

Name:

Handout 16A: Lyrics to "This Little Light of Mine"

Directions: Use these lyrics to follow along with the song.

This Little Light of Mine

This little light of mine, I'm gonna let it shine.
This little light of mine, I'm gonna let it shine.
This little light of mine, I'm gonna let it shine.
Every day, every day,
Every day, every day,
I'm gonna let my little light shine.

Everywhere I go, I'm gonna let it shine.
Everywhere I go, I'm gonna let it shine.
Everywhere I go, I'm gonna let it shine.
Every day, every day,
Every day, every day,
I'm gonna let my little light shine.

Deep down in the South, we're gonna let it shine.
Deep down in the South, we're gonna let it shine.
Deep down in the South, we're gonna let it shine.
Every day, every day,
Every day, every day,
I'm gonna let my little light shine.

Name:

Out on the highway, we're gonna let it shine.
Out on the highway, we're gonna let it shine.
Out on the highway, we're gonna let it shine.
Every day, every day,
Every day, every day,
We're gonna let our little light shine.

We have the light of freedom, we're gonna let it shine.
We have the light of freedom, we're gonna let it shine.
We have the light of freedom, we're gonna let it shine.
Every day, every day,
Every day, every day,
We're gonna let our little light shine.

This little light of mine, I'm gonna let it shine.
This little light of mine, I'm gonna let it shine.
This little light of mine, I'm gonna let it shine.
Every day, every day,
Every day, every day,
I'm gonna let my little light shine.

Written by Henry Dixon Loes, 1920

Name:

Handout 16B: SCAPE Chart

Directions: Write down words or phrases to name or describe the setting, characters, action, problem, and solution of the story. Use this chart when the action comes before the problem.

SCAPE Chart	
Text or Event:	
Setting	
Character	
Action	
Problem	
Ending	

Name:

Handout 16C: Shades of Meaning

Directions: Cut apart each row of words. Order the words from least strong to strongest on the word lines.

transform	change	switch
know	think	believe
speed	walk	hurry
yelled	howled	said
shoved	touched	pushed
would	could	should
moan	cry	sob
liked	enjoyed	loved

Name:

Handout 17A: Sentence Variety

Directions: Compare the two excerpts.

Excerpt Version One:

Ruby experienced that kind of school day every day, for weeks that turned into months.

She walked to the Frantz school surrounded by marshals. Ruby walked slowly for the first few blocks. She was wearing a clean dress and a bow in her hair and carrying her lunch pail. Ruby saw a crowd of people marching up and down the street as she approached the school.

Excerpt Version Two:

Every day, for weeks that turned into months, Ruby experienced that kind of school day.

She walked to the Frantz school surrounded by marshals. Wearing a clean dress and a bow in her hair and carrying her lunch pail, Ruby walked slowly for the first few blocks. As Ruby approached the school, she saw a crowd of people marching up and down the street.

Name: _____

Check for Understanding

Which paragraph has more variety?

A. *Ruby's mother took care of the children during the day. Ruby's mother went to work scrubbing floors in a bank after they were tucked in bed. Ruby's mother took the family to church every Sunday. Ruby's mother said, "We wanted our children to be near God's spirit."*

B. *Ruby's mother took care of the children during the day. After they were tucked into bed, she went to work scrubbing floors in a bank. Every Sunday, the family went to church. "We wanted our children to be near God's spirit," Ruby's mother said.*

Paragraph_____ has more variety because_____

_____

Why do writers rearrange sentences to add variety?

_____

_____

Name:

Handout 18A: Narrative Writing Checklist

Directions: After completing your informative paragraph, circle ☺ Yes or ☹ Not Yet to answer each prompt. Be sure to include a writing goal.

Reading Comprehension	Self	Peer	Teacher
I understand how Ruby Bridges responded to injustice.	☺ ☹ Yes Not Yet	☺ ☹ Yes Not Yet	☺ ☹ Yes Not Yet
Structure	Self	Peer	Teacher
I use all parts of the SCAPE. ☐ Setting ☐ Characters ☐ Action ☐ Problem ☐ Ending	☺ ☹ Yes Not Yet	☺ ☹ Yes Not Yet	☺ ☹ Yes Not Yet
Development	Self	Peer	Teacher
I use one (time) temporal word to tell the reader when events happen.	☺ ☹ Yes Not Yet	☺ ☹ Yes Not Yet	☺ ☹ Yes Not Yet

Name:

Style	Self		Peer		Teacher	
I rearrange a sentence with one adjective.	🙂 Yes	😐 Not Yet	🙂 Yes	😐 Not Yet	🙂 Yes	😐 Not Yet
I rearrange a sentence with one adverb.	🙂 Yes	😐 Not Yet	🙂 Yes	😐 Not Yet	🙂 Yes	😐 Not Yet
Conventions	**Self**		**Peer**		**Teacher**	
I use my best spelling. **A B C**	🙂 Yes	😐 Not Yet	🙂 Yes	😐 Not Yet	🙂 Yes	😐 Not Yet
I use end punctuation. **. ? !**	🙂 Yes	😐 Not Yet	🙂 Yes	😐 Not Yet	🙂 Yes	😐 Not Yet
I write complete sentences that have subjects and verbs.	🙂 Yes	😐 Not Yet	🙂 Yes	😐 Not Yet	🙂 Yes	😐 Not Yet
Total # of 🙂:						

Name:

_____

My writing goal is

_____

_____

_____

Teacher Feedback

Name:

Handout 19A: Narrative Comparison

Directions: Read both narratives. First, highlight the elements of SCAPE in the first narrative. Then, underline Ruby's thoughts and feelings in the second narrative.

Narrative #1

I am going to the Frantz Elementary School. My mom is walking with me. I see many white people yelling at us and holding signs. They do not want me to go to this school. The marshals keep us safe. I am going to walk in to the school quickly. I made it inside!

Narrative #2

I am scared to go to Frantz Elementary School. It makes me feel better to walk with my mom. I see many white people yelling at us and holding signs. Why are they being so mean? I don't understand why they do not want me to go to this school. The marshals keep us safe. That makes me feel better too. I want to cry but I will be brave. We try to get in the school quickly.

Name:

Handout 19B: Fluency Homework

Directions: Choose one of the text options to read for homework. Have an adult or peer initial the unshaded boxes each day that you read the passage.

Option A

At that time, black children and white children went to separate schools in New Orleans. The black children were not able to receive the same education as the white children. It wasn't fair. And it was against the nation's law.

40 words

Coles, Robert. *The Story of Ruby Bridges*. Illustrated by George Ford, 1995. Scholastic, 2010.

Student Performance Checklist:	Day 1 You	Listener*	Day 2 You	Listener*	Day 3 You	Listener*	Day 4 You	Listener*
Read the passage three to five times.								
Read with appropriate phrasing and pausing.								
Read with appropriate expression.								
Read at a good pace, not too fast and not too slow.								
Read to be heard and understood.								

*Adult or peer

Name:

Option B

Then one morning, something happened. Mrs. Henry stood by a window in her classroom as she usually did, watching Ruby walk toward the school. Suddenly, Ruby stopped—right in front of the mob of howling and screaming people. She stood there facing all those men and women. She seemed to be talking to them.

53 words

Coles, Robert. *The Story of Ruby Bridges*. Illustrated by George Ford, 1995. Scholastic, 2010.

Student Performance Checklist:	Day 1		Day 2		Day 3		Day 4	
	You	Listener*	You	Listener*	You	Listener*	You	Listener*
Read the passage three to five times.								
Read with appropriate phrasing and pausing.								
Read with appropriate expression.								
Read at a good pace, not too fast and not too slow.								
Read to be heard and understood.								

*Adult or peer

Name:

Handout 20A: Shades of Meaning

Directions: Cut out each row of words. Order the words from least strong to strongest on the word lines.

happy	joyful	ecstatic
anxious	frightened	terrified
strong	powerful	mighty
bad	mean	terrible
confident	brave	courageous
liked	enjoyed	loved

Name:

Handout 21A: SCPAE Chart

Directions: Write down words or phrases to name or describe the setting, characters, problem, action, and ending of the story. Use this chart when the problem comes before the action.

SCPAE Chart	
Text or Event:	
Setting	
Character	
Problem	
Action	
Ending	

Name:

Handout 21B: Sentence Variety

Directions: Cut out the sentence parts. Rearrange them to create at least two different sentences. Write down your sentences in your notebook.

Sentence One:

> something unusual happened
>
> as Mrs. Henry watched Ruby
>
> one morning

Sentence Two:

> suddenly
>
> in front of the angry mob
>
> Ruby stopped

Sentence Three:

> calmly
>
> she stood
>
> howling people
>
> facing the

Name:

Handout 22A: Sentence Variety

Directions:

1) Read the sentence and underline the adverb or adjective.

2) Rearrange and revise the sentence, placing and adverb or adjective at the beginning.

3) If needed, insert a comma in the right place.

- Ruby went to school eagerly each day.

_____

- The marshals watched Ruby frightened.

_____

- Dr. King spoke bravely to the crowd of people.

_____

- Ruby's mother watched her walk to school nervously.

_____

Name:

Development	Self		Peer		Teacher	
I add one detail to describe my characters' actions.	☺ Yes	😐 Not Yet	☺ Yes	😐 Not Yet	☺ Yes	😐 Not Yet
I add one detail to describe what my characters are thinking.	☺ Yes	😐 Not Yet	☺ Yes	😐 Not Yet	☺ Yes	😐 Not Yet
I add one detail to describe what my characters are feeling.	☺ Yes	😐 Not Yet	☺ Yes	😐 Not Yet	☺ Yes	😐 Not Yet
Style	**Self**		**Peer**		**Teacher**	
Rearrange a sentence using one adjective.	☺ Yes	😐 Not Yet	☺ Yes	😐 Not Yet	☺ Yes	😐 Not Yet
Rearrange a sentence using one adverb.	☺ Yes	😐 Not Yet	☺ Yes	😐 Not Yet	☺ Yes	😐 Not Yet
Conventions	**Self**		**Peer**		**Teacher**	
I use my best spelling. **A B C**	☺ Yes	😐 Not Yet	☺ Yes	😐 Not Yet	☺ Yes	😐 Not Yet

Name:

I use end punctuation. . ? !	😊 Yes 😐 Not Yet	😊 Yes 😐 Not Yet	😊 Yes 😐 Not Yet
I write complete sentences that have subjects and verbs.	😊 Yes 😐 Not Yet	😊 Yes 😐 Not Yet	😊 Yes 😐 Not Yet
Total # of 😊:			

My writing goal is

_____

_____

_____

Teacher Feedback

Name:

Handout 24A: Fluency Homework

Directions: Choose one of the text options to read for homework. Have an adult or peer initial the unshaded boxes each day that you read the passage.

Option A

Looking around, she saw that other children were smiling at her. By the end of the day, she had made a friend. And by the end of the school year, she had made many friends of different backgrounds. She knew that her family had fought for that.

47 words

Tonatiuh, Duncan. *Separate is Never Equal: Sylvia Mendez and Her Family's Fight for Desegregation*. Abrams Books for Young Readers, 2014.

Student Performance Checklist:	Day 1		Day 2		Day 3		Day 4	
	You	Listener*	You	Listener*	You	Listener*	You	Listener*
Read the passage three to five times.								
Read with appropriate phrasing and pausing.								
Read with appropriate expression.								
Read at a good pace, not too fast and not too slow.								
Read to be heard and understood.								

*Adult or peer

Name:

Option B

On March 2, 1945, Mr. Marcus went to the courthouse and filed the lawsuit. The trial was held at a courthouse in Los Angeles. Sylvia and her family dressed in their best clothes and sat in the courtroom to listen. The hearing lasted five days.

45 words

Tonatiuh, Duncan. *Separate is Never Equal: Sylvia Mendez and Her Family's Fight for Desegregation.* **Abrams Books for Young Readers, 2014.**

Student Performance Checklist:	Day 1		Day 2		Day 3		Day 4	
	You	Listener*	You	Listener*	You	Listener*	You	Listener*
Read the passage three to five times.								
Read with appropriate phrasing and pausing.								
Read with appropriate expression.								
Read at a good pace, not too fast and not too slow.								
Read to be heard and understood.								

*Adult or peer

Name:

Handout 24B: Compound Words

Directions: Determine the definition of the underlined words in the following sentences.

1. At <u>mealtime</u>, there was no one else for Ruby to eat lunch with.

2. Ruby walked along the <u>sidewalk</u> to school.

3. There is a <u>flowerpot</u> on the shelf in Ruby's classroom.

4. Ruby carried a <u>lunchbox</u> to school.

5. Ruby went to the <u>classroom</u> with a big smile on her face.

6. Ruby Bridges is now a successful <u>businesswoman</u>.

Choose one compound word. How did you determine its meaning?

_____

_____

Name:

Handout 27A: Response Cards

Beginning Sylvia's actions and words	**Beginning** Mrs. Mendez's actions and words
For the rest of the day, Sylvia did not speak or introduce herself in her classes. She kept her head down when walking in the halls. She told her mother, "I don't want to go to that school anymore. The kids are mean."	Sylvia, "¿No sabes que por eso luchamos?" Don't you know that is why we fought?
Ending Sylvia's actions and words	**Ending** Mrs. Mendez's actions and words
The next day, she returned to the Westminster school. This time she did not listen to any whispers. She ignored the children who pointed at her and called her names. Instead, she held her head high.	"...we fought to make sure you could attend a good school and have equal opportunities."

Name:

Handout 28A: Narrative Writing Checklist

Directions: After completing your informative paragraph, circle 😊 Yes or 😐 Not Yet to answer each prompt. Be sure to include a writing goal.

Reading Comprehension	Self	Peer	Teacher
I understand how Sylvia Mendez responded to injustice.	😊 😐 Yes Not Yet	😊 😐 Yes Not Yet	😊 😐 Yes Not Yet
Structure	**Self**	**Peer**	**Teacher**
I use all parts of the SCAPE. ☐ Setting ☐ Characters ☐ Action ☐ Problem ☐ Ending	😊 😐 Yes Not Yet	😊 😐 Yes Not Yet	😊 😐 Yes Not Yet
I use one (time) temporal word to tell my reader when events happen.	😊 😐 Yes Not Yet	😊 😐 Yes Not Yet	😊 😐 Yes Not Yet
I provide a sense of closure at the end.	😊 😐 Yes Not Yet	😊 😐 Yes Not Yet	😊 😐 Yes Not Yet

Name:

Development	Self		Peer		Teacher	
I add one detail to describe my characters' actions.	☺ Yes	☹ Not Yet	☺ Yes	☹ Not Yet	☺ Yes	☹ Not Yet
I add one detail to describe what my characters are thinking.	☺ Yes	☹ Not Yet	☺ Yes	☹ Not Yet	☺ Yes	☹ Not Yet
I add one detail to describe what my characters are feeling.	☺ Yes	☹ Not Yet	☺ Yes	☹ Not Yet	☺ Yes	☹ Not Yet
Style	**Self**		**Peer**		**Teacher**	
Rearrange a sentence using one adjective.	☺ Yes	☹ Not Yet	☺ Yes	☹ Not Yet	☺ Yes	☹ Not Yet
Rearrange a sentence using one adverb.	☺ Yes	☹ Not Yet	☺ Yes	☹ Not Yet	☺ Yes	☹ Not Yet
Conventions	**Self**		**Peer**		**Teacher**	
I use my best spelling. **A B C**	☺ Yes	☹ Not Yet	☺ Yes	☹ Not Yet	☺ Yes	☹ Not Yet

Name:

I use end punctuation. . ? !	☺ Yes 😐 Not Yet	☺ Yes 😐 Not Yet	☺ Yes 😐 Not Yet
I write complete sentences that have subjects and verbs.	☺ Yes 😐 Not Yet	☺ Yes 😐 Not Yet	☺ Yes 😐 Not Yet
Total # of ☺:			

My writing goal is

_____

_____

Teacher Feedback

Name:

Handout 28B: Compound Words

Directions: Determine the definition of the underlined words in the following sentences from and about *Separate is Never Equal.*

1. One day, a truck driver <u>overheard</u> Mr. Mendez trying to convince a worker to sign his petition.

2. There was a <u>playground</u> with monkey bars and a red swing.

3. The Mendez victory made the newspaper <u>headlines</u>.

4. He was a <u>businessman</u>, and he was used to dealing with people.

5. Sylvia's family sat in the <u>courtroom</u> and listed to the judge.

6. Sylvia made friends with her <u>classmates</u> at Westminster school.

Choose one compound word. How did you determine its meaning?

_____

_____

Name:

Handout 29A: Prefixes *bi–* and *tri–*

Directions: Circle the prefix in each underlined word. Then, fill in each blank with the correct number.

- Something that happens <u>biweekly</u> can happen every ____ weeks.

- Something that happens <u>triweekly</u> can happen every ____ weeks.

- How many wings does a <u>biplane</u> have? ____

- A <u>trilogy</u> is a movie or book with ____ parts.

- A <u>triplet</u> is a set of ____ .

- When you <u>bisect</u> something, you divide it into ____ parts.

- When you <u>trisect</u> something, you divide it into ____ parts.

- How many horns does a <u>triceratops</u> have? ____

- How many sports are in a <u>triathlon</u>? ____

- Can you think of any other words with *bi–* and *tri–*?

Name:

Check for Understanding: Define the words below.

Bilingual: _____

Trilingual: _____

Triangle: _____

Name:

Handout 31A: End-of-Module Task Pre-Writing

Directions: Work with a partner to complete the following questions. Take notes using words, phrases, and pictures.

Who are you?

Name the problem you are facing.

Describe your thoughts and feelings.

thoughts

Name:

Describe your thoughts and feelings.

feelings

How do you <u>respond</u> to injustice?

actions

Name:

Handout 33A: Narrative Writing Checklist

Directions: After completing your informative paragraph, circle ☺ Yes or ☹ Not Yet to answer each prompt. Be sure to include a writing goal.

Reading Comprehension	Self	Peer	Teacher
I understand how important historical people responded to injustice.	☺ ☹ Yes Not Yet	☺ ☹ Yes Not Yet	☺ ☹ Yes Not Yet
Structure	**Self**	**Peer**	**Teacher**
I use all parts of the SCAPE. ☐ Setting ☐ Characters ☐ Action ☐ Problem ☐ Ending	☺ ☹ Yes Not Yet	☺ ☹ Yes Not Yet	☺ ☹ Yes Not Yet
I use one (time) temporal word to tell my reader when events happen.	☺ ☹ Yes Not Yet	☺ ☹ Yes Not Yet	☺ ☹ Yes Not Yet
I provide a sense of closure at the end.	☺ ☹ Yes Not Yet	☺ ☹ Yes Not Yet	☺ ☹ Yes Not Yet

Name:

Development	Self		Peer		Teacher	
I add one detail to describe my characters' actions.	☺ Yes	😐 Not Yet	☺ Yes	😐 Not Yet	☺ Yes	😐 Not Yet
I add one detail to describe what my characters are thinking.	☺ Yes	😐 Not Yet	☺ Yes	😐 Not Yet	☺ Yes	😐 Not Yet
I add one detail to describe what my characters are feeling.	☺ Yes	😐 Not Yet	☺ Yes	😐 Not Yet	☺ Yes	😐 Not Yet
Style	**Self**		**Peer**		**Teacher**	
Rearrange a sentence using one adjective.	☺ Yes	😐 Not Yet	☺ Yes	😐 Not Yet	☺ Yes	😐 Not Yet
Rearrange a sentence using one adverb.	☺ Yes	😐 Not Yet	☺ Yes	😐 Not Yet	☺ Yes	😐 Not Yet
Conventions	**Self**		**Peer**		**Teacher**	
I use my best spelling. **A B C**	☺ Yes	😐 Not Yet	☺ Yes	😐 Not Yet	☺ Yes	😐 Not Yet

Name:

I use end punctuation. . ? !	😊 Yes 😐 Not Yet	😊 Yes 😐 Not Yet	😊 Yes 😐 Not Yet
I write complete sentences that have subjects and verbs.	😊 Yes 😐 Not Yet	😊 Yes 😐 Not Yet	😊 Yes 😐 Not Yet
Total # of 😊:			

My writing goal is

_____

_____

_____

Teacher Feedback

Name:

Handout 34A: Socratic Seminar Self-Reflection

Directions: Use one of the letters below to describe how often you performed each action during the Socratic Seminar.

A = I always did that.

S = I sometimes did that.

N = I'll do that next time.

Expectation	Evaluation (A, S, N)
I spoke on topic.	
I noticed the whole message.	
I linked what I said to what others said.	
I looked at the speaker.	
I spoke only when no one else was speaking.	
I used kind words.	

Volume of Reading Reflection Questions

Civil Rights Heroes, Grade 2, Module 3

Student Name: _____

Text: _____

Author: _____

Topic: _____

Genre/type of book:

Share your knowledge about the Civil Rights Movement by responding to the questions below.

Informational

1. **Wonder:** After looking at the cover of this book, what do you notice? What do you wonder?

2. **Organize:** What topics did this book cover about the Civil Rights Movement? What details made it interesting?

3. **Reveal:** How does the author use images to teach you important ideas about the Civil Rights Movement? Choose an image (e.g., photograph, map, or diagram) in the book that shows this important idea.

4. **Distill:** What big idea did the author want you to take away from reading this book? Find the page or line that most strongly communicates that big idea.

5. **Know:** What important points did you learn by reading this book? Think about a similar book to this one that you read in class. How are the important points similar or different to the points in this book?

6. **Vocabulary:** Create a list with three important words in this text. Draw a symbol to go with each word to help you remember the meaning of the word.

Literary

1. **Wonder:** What details do you notice about the cover that give you clues to what this story will be about?

2. **Organize:** What's happening in the text? Retell the story to a friend. Find a place where characters are using dialogue. Ask a friend or parent to read a different part of dialogue. Try to imagine the way you would use your voice in that scene.

3. **Reveal:** How does the author use interesting words and phrases in the story help you understand what life was like for the characters in the story? Does the author use any repetition in the book? Give examples.

4. **Distill:** How did the main character change from the beginning to the end of the book? Draw a picture to show how the character was at the beginning of the story and another picture to show how the character was at the end of the story.

5. **Know:** How does this story add to what you have learned about the Civil Rights Movement from other stories or books? Have you learned more about the Civil Rights Movement from stories or informational texts? Why?

6. **Vocabulary:** Choose three words from the story that describe what it was like to live during this period of history. Draw a quick sketch to go with each word.

OUR CLASS WILL WATCH THESE VIDEOS:

- "Ruby Bridges Interview"
- "Civil Rights – Ruby Bridges"
- "The Man Who Changed America"
- "Sylvia Mendez and Sandra Mendez Duran"
- "The Freedom Singers Perform at the White House"

OUR CLASS WILL LISTEN TO THESE SONGS:

- "Ain't Gonna Let Nobody Turn Me Around"
- "This Little Light of Mine"
- "America (My Country Tis of Thee)"

OUR CLASS WILL ASK THESE QUESTIONS:

- What injustices did people face before the Civil Rights Act of 1964?
- What was Martin Luther King Jr.'s dream for the world?
- How did Ruby Bridges respond to injustice?
- How did the Mendez family respond to injustice?

QUESTIONS TO ASK AT HOME:

As you read with your Grade 2 student, ask:

- What is the essential meaning, or most important message, in this book?

BOOKS TO READ AT HOME:

Biography

- *Martin's Big Words*, Doreen Rappaport
- *Heart on Fire: Susan B. Anthony Votes for President*, Ann Malaspina
- *Abraham Lincoln: Lawyer, Leader, Legend*, Justine and Ron Fontes
- *I Have a Dream*, Martin Luther King, Jr

Historical Account

- *Sit-In: How Four Friends Stood Up By Sitting Down*, Andrea Davis Pinkney
- *Freedom on the Menu: The Greensboro Sit-Ins*, Carole Boston Weatherford
- *The Case for Loving: The Fight for Interracial Marriage*, Selina Alko

Picture Books

- *Henry's Freedom Box: A True Story from the Underground Railroad*, Ellen Levine
- *Two Friends: Susan B. Anthony and Frederick Douglass*, Dean Robbins
- *I Could Do That! Ester Morris Gets Women the Vote*, Linda Arms White
- *A is for Abigail: An Almanac of Amazing American Women*, Lynne Cheney
- *The Listeners*, Gloria Whelan

IDEAS FOR TALKING ABOUT CIVIL RIGHTS HEROES:

Visit the library together. Ask the librarian to recommend a book on Civil Rights, or select one of the titles in the list above. Take a look at the illustrations with your second grader and ask:

- What do you notice and wonder about this illustration?
- Is this character a hero?
- How did this person respond to injustice?

CREDITS

Great Minds® has made every effort to obtain permission for the reprinting of all copyrighted material. If any owner of copyrighted material is not acknowledged herein, please contact Great Minds® for proper acknowledgment in all future editions and reprints of this module.

- All images are used under license from Shutterstock.com unless otherwise noted.

- All material from the *Common Core State Standards for English Language Arts & Literacy in History/Social Studies, Science, and Technical Subjects* © Copyright 2010 National Governors Association Center for Best Practices and Council of Chief State School Officers. All rights reserved.

- Handout 14A: "Words Like Freedom" from *The Collected Poems of Langston Hughes* by Langston Hughes, edited by Arnold Rampersad with David Roessel, Associate Editor, copyright © 1994 by the Estate of Langston Hughes. Used by permission of Alfred A. Knopf, an imprint of the Knopf Doubleday Publishing Group, a division of Penguin Random House LLC. All rights reserved. Any third party use of this material, outside of this publication, is prohibited. Interested parties must apply directly to Penguin Random House LLC for permission.

- Assessment 18A: "Dreams" from *The Collected Poems of Langston Hughes* by Langston Hughes, edited by Arnold Rampersad with David Roessel, Associate Editor, copyright © 1994 by the Estate of Langston Hughes. Used by permission of Alfred A. Knopf, an imprint of the Knopf Doubleday Publishing Group, a division of Penguin Random House LLC. All rights reserved. Any third party use of this material, outside of this publication, is prohibited. Interested parties must apply directly to Penguin Random House LLC for permission.

- Assessment 30A: "Different Voices" by Anna Gratz Cockerille from *Kids Fight for Civil Rights*, Appleseeds October 2013. Text copyright © 2013 by Carus Publishing Company. Reprinted by permission of Cricket Media. All Cricket Media material is copyrighted by Carus Publishing d/b/a Cricket Media, and/or various authors and illustrators. Any commercial use or distribution of material without permission is strictly prohibited. Please visit (**http://www.cricketmedia.com/info/licensing2**) for licensing and (**http://www.cricketmedia.com**) for subscriptions

- Assessment 31A: "When Peace Met Power" by Laura Helweg from *Kids Fight for Civil Rights*, Appleseeds October 2013. Text copyright © 2013 by Carus Publishing Company. Reprinted by permission of Cricket Media. All Cricket Media material is copyrighted by Carus Publishing d/b/a Cricket Media, and/or various authors and illustrators. Any commercial use or distribution of material without permission is strictly prohibited. Please visit (**http://www.cricketmedia.com/info/licensing2**) for licensing and (**http://www.cricketmedia.com**) for subscriptions

- For updated credit information, please visit **http://witeng.link/credits**.

ACKNOWLEDGMENTS

Great Minds® Staff

The following writers, editors, reviewers, and support staff contributed to the development of this curriculum.

Ann Brigham, Lauren Chapalee, Sara Clarke, Emily Climer, Lorraine Griffith, Emily Gula, Sarah Henchey, Trish Huerster, Stephanie Kane-Mainier, Lior Klirs, Liz Manolis, Andrea Minich, Lynne Munson, Marya Myers, Rachel Rooney, Aaron Schifrin, Danielle Shylit, Rachel Stack, Sarah Turnage, Michelle Warner, Amy Wierzbicki, Margaret Wilson, and Sarah Woodard.

Colleagues and Contributors

We are grateful for the many educators, writers, and subject-matter experts who made this program possible.

David Abel, Robin Agurkis, Elizabeth Bailey, Julianne Barto, Amy Benjamin, Andrew Biemiller, Charlotte Boucher, Sheila Byrd-Carmichael, Eric Carey, Jessica Carloni, Janine Cody, Rebecca Cohen, Elaine Collins, Tequila Cornelious, Beverly Davis, Matt Davis, Thomas Easterling, Jeanette Edelstein, Kristy Ellis, Moira Clarkin Evans, Charles Fischer, Marty Gephart, Kath Gibbs, Natalie Goldstein, Christina Gonzalez, Mamie Goodson, Nora Graham, Lindsay Griffith, Brenna Haffner, Joanna Hawkins, Elizabeth Haydel, Steve Hettleman, Cara Hoppe, Ashley Hymel, Carol Jago, Jennifer Johnson, Mason Judy, Gail Kearns, Shelly Knupp, Sarah Kushner, Shannon Last, Suzanne Lauchaire, Diana Leddy, David Liben, Farren Liben, Jennifer Marin, Susannah Maynard, Cathy McGath, Emily McKean, Jane Miller, Rebecca Moore, Cathy Newton, Turi Nilsson, Julie Norris, Galemarie Ola, Michelle Palmieri, Meredith Phillips, Shilpa Raman, Tonya Romayne, Emmet Rosenfeld, Jennifer Ruppel, Mike Russoniello, Deborah Samley, Casey Schultz, Renee Simpson, Rebecca Sklepovich, Amelia Swabb, Kim Taylor, Vicki Taylor, Melissa Thomson, Lindsay Tomlinson, Melissa Vail, Keenan Walsh, Julia Wasson, Lynn Welch, Yvonne Guerrero Welch, Emily Whyte, Lynn Woods, and Rachel Zindler.

Early Adopters

The following early adopters provided invaluable insight and guidance for Wit & Wisdom:

- Bourbonnais School District 53 • Bourbonnais, IL
- Coney Island Prep Middle School • Brooklyn, NY
- Gate City Charter School for the Arts • Merrimack, NH
- Hebrew Academy for Special Children • Brooklyn, NY
- Paris Independent Schools • Paris, KY
- Saydel Community School District • Saydel, IA
- Strive Collegiate Academy • Nashville, TN
- Valiente College Preparatory Charter School • South Gate, CA
- Voyageur Academy • Detroit, MI

Design Direction provided by Alton Creative, Inc.

Project management support, production design, and copyediting services provided by ScribeConcepts.com

Copyediting services provided by Fine Lines Editing

Product management support provided by Sandhill Consulting